MONORAILS

Although its history goes back to 1824, the monorail may become the normal mode of short-distance travel in ten or twenty years. In this fascinating history of monorails, G. T. Harvey takes us for a ride on the "Peg-Leg" Railroad, the Listowel & Ballybunion Railway and the famous miniature monorail at Disneyland, all forerunners of the future. The book covers a wide selection of past and present projects and is illustrated with over fifty photographs and drawings.

MONORAILS

by

Derek G. T. Harvey

with illustrations by Leigh Hunt

G. P. Putnam's Sons　　　New York

ACKNOWLEDGMENTS

For the assistance I have received in the preparation of this book, my grateful acknowledgments are due to Alweg GmbH; the Düsseldorfer Nachrichten; the Hunslet Engine Co., Ltd.; *La Vie du Rail*; Lockheed Aircraft International, Inc.; Railplanes, Ltd.; the *Railway Gazette*; SAFEGE Transport; the Stadtverwaltung, Wuppertal; Tokyo Shibaura Electric Co., Ltd.; the Wegematic Corporation; Wuppertaler Stadtwerke, AG; and Mr. John R. Day whose books, *Unusual Railways* and *More Unusual Railways,* proved an invaluable source of reference.

CONTENTS

INTRODUCTION

This is a brief history of engineering achievement and failure in a field that few people know much about. A few years ago if you asked someone what a monorail looked like, the chances were he wouldn't even know what it was, let alone have seen one. Even today, most of us have to think twice before we answer: Well, let's see, it's a kind of a railroad car with two wheels — er, no, maybe a row of wheels, kind of balancing on a single rail, like a tightrope walker. What's the advantage? The average person is not too sure; he looks on a monorail as some new travel gimmick introduced at one or two major fairgrounds, a nuclear-age novelty for the sightseers.

He is partly right. Only two monorails have ever operated for any length of time as everyday means of transportation. Yet in the last 150 years or so, no less than 90 such lines have been projected in various parts of the world. Admittedly, less than half of these designs ever got much beyond the inventor's drawing board, and only seventeen succeeded in carrying fare-paying passengers.

Most monorails have either met with a spectacular accident or have bankrupted their owners, or they simply faded away for lack of support. But their story is nonetheless worth telling, if only for the ingenuity and resourcefulness and determination of the men who built them; and to illustrate the evolution of the modern monorail from the ashes of these long-forgotten projects.

Compared with orthodox railroads, monorail systems have, from the beginning, been cheaper and quicker to build — or so it was claimed. And quite a few of them were. The majority of the early cars and locomotives, however, were too complex and unreliable, or hopelessly impractical, or wildly unsafe. The public didn't trust them and the financiers wouldn't back them.

For many years, the monorail's greatest advantage in densely populated areas — of taking up less ground space than a conventional railroad or elevated system — was not exploited. Few people wanted a new and untried method of transportation when there was nothing wrong with the old ones. So, as cities expanded toward their suburbs, bus and trolley car services were extended, and in some places new elevated railroads were built. In New York, London, Paris and Moscow they went underground, too, in a vast and costly network of deep tunnels bored through soil and rock and under rivers. Later on came the miles of new suburban highways to speed the increasing flow of automobiles. And still the commuter traffic grew denser and denser.

It is only since World War II that the big cities have shown unmistakable signs of becoming finally and hopelessly choked. Millions are being spent on road improvements, but these temporary remedies hardly become effective before they are swamped in the flood tide of increasing traffic. The planners have learned the hard way, that not only does the population of large cities expand three to four times faster than in the rest of the country, but traffic problems in these cities grows three times faster than the population.

The increasing popularity of air travel only adds to the tangle. For it is the cities that provide the greatest number of passengers, with airline buses joining the hordes of automobiles and taxis in the frequently more than one-hour crawl between city center and airport — a period in which the frustrated traveler could have flown several hundreds of miles. A helicopter service is not the complete answer. Even when radio and radar aids make the helicopter independent of weather conditions, it will never be able to compete with surface transport in seating capacity and cost.

Tunneling is also much too expensive, and there isn't space for enough new suburban highways.

In France, for example, road congestion is costing the country $140,000,000 a year. The traffic jams have become a critical problem, and something drastic has to be done. The obvious solution is to go upward, to build more elevated railroads of the traditional type. But these tend to be cumbersome and noisy and spoil the look of the city.

So the transportation engineers have gone back through their history books and revived the idea of a monorail, using the latest techniques of railroad, automobile and airplane engineering. Designed with

8

the help of electronic computers, tested in laboratories, developed on the test track, today's monorails are fast, safe and almost silent. They have not yet scored any widescale commercial success for their manufacturers because, of course, it takes time for any city to make up its mind on such a major issue. Many different civic and government authorities are involved in planning the route, negotiating right of way with property owners, integrating the new service with existing transportation, and voting the necessary funds. These plans amount to some two or three million dollars per mile; and although the price may seem small for easing the traffic chaos, it is still a large sum of money from the taxpayers' pockets.

But after a year or two in which their future has appeared to hang in the balance, monorails have recently begun to catch on in one country after another. And there seems every possibility that in ten or twenty years time they will be regarded by many commuters and airline passengers as a normal method of short-distance travel.

Perhaps by that time monorails won't run on wheels or be driven by motors as we know them — or, for that matter, be controlled by a driver in the cab. Already there are designs for driverless, automatically controlled trains, hurled along an elevated beamway by powerful electromagnets, with a cushion of compressed air taking the place of wheels.

Therefore, in case we should take these engineering marvels for granted, let us turn back the pages of history to the days of the horse carriage — to the time when inventors, lacking technical expertise, used only their imagination to design weird and wonderful machines, and then built them to see whether they would work — back to England, in the year 1824.

CHAPTER 1

THE FIRST MONORAIL, 1824

Some of the fiercest arguments in engineering history evolved over claims to having built the first *this* or *that* in the world — the first airplane, the first automobile, the first diesel motor. The monorail is no exception. But no one can trace any earlier documentary evidence of this method of transport than that provided by a British patent specification, dated November 22, 1821. Describing "an improvement in the construction of railways," the document refers to "the substitution of a single line of rail, supported at such a height from the ground as to allow the centre of gravity of the carriages to be below the upper surface of the rail." Nowadays we would just call it a monorail.

The proposal came from Henry Robinson Palmer who, as engineer to the London Dock Company, was concerned with the loading and unloading of ships. His first line, erected in 1824 in the London docks to carry merchandise, was built mostly from ships' timbers.

Stout oak posts were driven into the ground at heights varying according to the undulations of the terrain so that their tops ran level. The rail itself was made of planks, set on edge in notches in the tops of the posts, and protected by an iron capping. The wagons ran on two cast-iron wheels, one behind the other, with deep flanges to prevent them from slipping off the rail and hung down on either side of the rail. Balancing this seesaw with equal loads on either side must have given the dockers plenty to swear about. Seven of these swaying contraptions made up a train, which was drawn by a horse pulling from one side on a tow rope, after the manner of the canal barges of the day.

Indeed, the whole affair looked so shaky that people began to ask whether it had any real advantage, other than novelty, over a conventional twin-rail track. But Palmer was able to show how cheaply and quickly it had been built, and to prove from resistance tests he had carried out on several orthodox trains of that period that they required at least twice as much pulling as a monorail train of the same weight. Wheel bearings in those days must have had plenty of friction; the argument certainly wouldn't hold nowadays.

Before long, a similar line was built to carry bricks across the Cheshunt marshes from the brickworks to the barges on the River Lee. An elegant carriage was constructed for the grand opening of the Cheshunt Railway on June 25, 1825, and with great ceremony it carried the officials of the company along the line — the first passengers to be transported by monorail, and the last on this line.

A year later, the inventor exhibited a model in Germany, and a company was formed to build a Palmer line between Elberfeld and Barmen for carrying coal. Work was never started on this project, but by curious coincidence an overhead railway was built on this very route three-quarters of a century later — a monorail which is still in service today. Perhaps there was some definite link between the two, but none has ever been discovered.

The first monorail passengers, at the grand opening of the Cheshunt Railway on June 25, 1825. From a contemporary print.

CHAPTER 2

ANDRAUD'S "ATMOSPHERIC RAILWAY," 1856

Apart from a number of improvements on Palmer's patent, and a few enthusiastic if quaintly improbable designs, the next fifty years saw little practical progress in monorail technique. In fact, only one was built during this period, and even this appears to have met with no success. After trials of a reduced-scale version had been conducted in the Paris Champs Elysées in 1856, no more was heard of it.

But its strange details are worth recording, if only for the ingenuity of its inventor, whose name was Andraud. The rail was an I-section iron girder supported, like Palmer's, on wooden posts of varying length to suit the ups and downs of the ground. The split carriages hung on either side of the rail from a pair of wheels in line. Each half carriage looked something like a Wells Fargo stagecoach, with seats for four passengers inside and two more on the roof between the main wheels. To prevent the carriages from swaying from side to side, there also appears to have been a guide rail running between the split in the carriages and presumably connecting with auxiliary wheels on either side — a principle born of experience with the Palmer lines, and subsequently adopted in every straddle monorail right up to the present day.

Whether or not ideas such as these were copied by successive engineers or were re-invented is hard to say. However, Andraud's source of motive power was original, to say the least. It was worked by two long rubber tubes, one on either side of the girder rail, and gripped tightly by a pair of vertical rollers on the front carriage. Compressed air was pumped into the tubes from one end of the line, and as they expanded they were supposed to squeeze the train along. It seems they didn't.

Andraud's Atmospheric Railway — an impression of how it might have looked. A reduced-scale version was demonstrated in Paris in 1856, driven by compressed air.

CHAPTER 3

THE "PEG-LEG" RAILROAD, 1876

Active work started in America in 1876 with a demonstration at the Centennial Exposition in Philadelphia of a steam-driven monorail, the invention of General Le-Roy Stone. The rail rested on longitudinal wooden sleepers, supported at intervals by A-shaped cast-iron frames 10 feet high, with two stabilizing rails at the crossbars of the A. The locomotive had two main wheels, the rear one driven by a rotary steam engine. How this worked is not recorded beyond the fact that it had no piston or crank, so one might imagine it to have been some form of bucket-wheel turbine attached to the driving wheel. It hauled, rather slowly it seems, a train of monstrous double-decker carriages, mounted pannier-fashion on either side of the track.

By 1878 a four-mile line had been built along the valley of the Foster Brook, between Bradford and Gilmore, Pennsylvania, together with two more trains. Its main object was the transport of oil-drilling equipment and personnel to Derrick City, but wayside stations were hurriedly erected at Tarpot, Babcock's Mill and Harrisburg Run, and local inhabitants began to ride the line. This did not suit the existing narrow-gauge railroad that ran parallel to it, and before long the two rival companies were taking turns in cutting their fares and racing each other along the valley.

To quote from the *Historical Bradford:* "Races between the Peg-leg and the Narrow Gauge were frequent. The spectacle was worth witnessing. The Narrow Gauge, its bantam locomotive puffing and snorting like an over-trained racehorse, and the Peg-leg with its unique equipment, which an Irishman wittily described as 'a train of cars running on a fence' humming round the snaky curves like a bicycle scorcher on the home stretch, unquestion-

15

The turbine-driven Peg-Leg locomotive hauled oil-drilling
equipment to Derrick City. Artist's impression, from an early
photograph.

ably was a sight that afforded the passengers plenty of diversion."

The rotary locomotives, however, lacked power and were no match for their orthodox rivals. The oil excitement was also beginning to die, and with its revenue growing smaller and smaller, the Bradford & Foster Brook Company decided to gamble on a much larger locomotive driven by conventional pistons.

On the fateful morning of January 27, 1879, the 15-ton flyer, steam roaring from its safety valve, was coupled to a flat wagon and a carful of officials, and set off down the line at a cracking pace. A few minutes later there came a shattering explosion as the boiler burst, and the train crashed over into the creek, killing the driver and fireman and three passengers, and severely injuring the rest.

This was the end of the Peg-Leg, which was sold a month later, resold the following year, and finally abandoned.

The ill-fated Bradford & Foster Brook locomotive which exploded during a demonstration run.

CHAPTER 4

MEIGS' MONORAIL, 1886

A couple of years before the Peg-Leg's first appearance in Philadelphia, a Captain J. V. Meigs, of Lowell, Massachusetts, had patented an elevated railway system of his own. It used two rails, mounted one above the other on a single line of supports — like Palmer's, only taller. This gave it the advantage over the more conventional New York elevated railway, claimed Meigs, of occupying very little ground space, which was already at a premium in cities and the populous parts of towns.

Meigs must have been a fine engineer as well as a far-sighted inventor, for his futuristic streamlined train, shaped like a tube to "diminish wind resistance and stresses," was full of mechanical wizardry that really worked.

The cylindrical locomotive and tender, and each of the 50-foot cars, was carried on two four-wheeled bogies whose axles were inclined downwards at about 45 degrees, canting the wheels inwards so that their lower flanges bore on either side of the same rail — the lower rail.

These wheels simply carried the weight. The driving was done by a separate pair of wheels in the center of the locomotive, mounted horizontally and gripping the upper rail like pincers. Each wheel, driven by a single-cylinder steam engine, was forced inwards onto the rail by a hydraulic cylinder and ram acting on its sliding axle box, the pressure of the fluid — glycerine — being controlled by the driver. Not only did this make adhesion independent of the weight of the locomotive, but the deep flanges on these horizontal wheels made it virtually impossible for the train to be derailed. Hydraulic action was also used for the steam regulators, reversing control brakes and the automatic coupling of the entire train.

Shaped like a tube to reduce wind resistance, Meigs' monorail was full of mechanical wizardry that really worked.

The fireman was in the usual position at the rear of the locomotive, where he could stoke the boiler. But the driver was up front in a raised compartment that looked like the wheelhouse of a ship, surrounded by a fearsome array of hydraulic control levers, gauges and dials, with ship-style voice tubes linking him with the fireman and the guard.

Perhaps these innovations were too far ahead of their time. Or it may have been the mechanical complexity and cost that frightened investors off Meigs' monorail and led them to dismiss his streamlined cars as a passing novelty. Although an experimental mile of track was built in East Cambridge in 1886, and a train was successfully demonstrated at speeds of up to 30 m.p.h., the project failed to stimulate sufficient interest, and eventually was abandoned.

Side view and cross-section of the Meigs car. Note the padded upholstery and inclined wheels. Based on drawings in a paper by Francis E. Galloupe to the American Society of Mechanical Engineers, 1886.

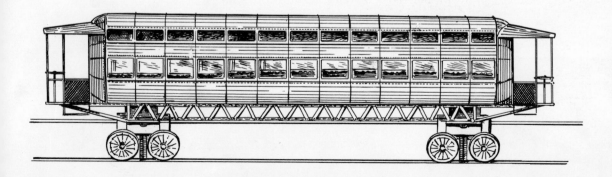

CHAPTER 5

ENOS ELECTRIC RAILWAY, 1887

Up until this time, all monorails had been of the supported type, riding on or straddling the running rail. In 1887, however, the Enos Electric Railway Company came forward with a different method, in which only the running gear was above the rail, the cars being suspended below for natural stability. (The relative merits of the two forms of construction are still being debated today, and both have their modern counterparts in the rival Alweg and SAFEGE systems which are described later.)

A 1,000-foot length of Enos track was erected in the works of the Daft Electric Light Company, an early power station at Greenville, New Jersey. It was built of light, open steelwork instead of using massive wooden beams, which it was thought would tend to make the streets dark and gloomy. The running gear consisted of two three-wheel bogies, each center wheel forming an integral part of an electric driving motor which picked up its current by rolling contact with the insulated rail. The car, which held sixty passengers, was suspended from the bogies by frames and rods, and was prevented from swaying by roof-mounted guide wheels which, like Meigs', ran on a second track positioned below the main rail. These wheels were also used to return the motor current to earth.

The Greenville demonstrations attracted considerable publicity in the press, and before long a group of businessmen in St. Paul, Minnesota, formed a company to build and operate such a line in their own town. The first move by the St. Paul Rapid Transit Company was to build a three-quarter-mile track in the suburb of South Park. Right from the start, their operations were hampered by lack of money. Timber was used instead of steel, and additional struts had to be fitted to stop the track from

The Enos Electric Railway, from a drawing in the *Electrical World*, U.S.A., 1887. The system was successfully demonstrated at Greenville, N.J., in the works of the Daft Electric Light Company.

The Enos line, as built at St. Paul, Minnesota. Timber was used instead of steel, and the car only just cleared the ground instead of being carried high above the traffic. From a contemporary drawing in *Engineering and Building Record*.

sagging under the weight of the car, which only just cleared the ground instead of being carried high above the traffic and the heads of the people passing by. The car itself was smaller than the Greenville prototype, holding only a dozen passengers, and had a top speed of about 12 m.p.h.

Even before this line had been completed, the go-ahead company had negotiated a franchise from the city council, in the face of stiff opposition, to build another line, running across the Mississippi into St. Paul and Minneapolis. Work on it was never started, presumably due to shortage of funds and the failure of the South Park elevated to make a profit. But the principle of a suspended monorail seems to have proved itself in the minds of engineers, for it appeared again in Germany a few years later.

CHAPTER 6

THE EARLY LARTIGUE LINES, 1876-1886

Turning back the pages of history nearly twenty years, and crossing the Atlantic, we find a Frenchman named Lartigue working on the esparto grass plantations in Algeria. Back in the eighteen-seventies, the grass was still carried by camels — a leisurely procession that irritated the young Frenchman. The story goes that he was thinking one day of ways in which the crop could be transported more quickly, and was watching an approaching camel train when he suddenly hit on an idea. Why not, he wondered, replace the long legs of the camels with thin iron trestles and their humps with wheels; and substitute a pannier car for the esparto wallets that hung down on either side of the animals?

This he did. And by 1876, a sixty-mile length of Lartigue line was operating in Algeria and another in Tunisia, the trucks pulled by mules.

But if the story of the invention is true, Lartigue must have been unaware that in 1869 J. L. Haddon, who was Director of Public Works in Syria, had already replaced mule transport by a steam monorail of his own design. The pannier wagons and the locomotive, which had a pair of upright boilers, hung down on either side of the rail from their central wheels, with horizontal rollers running on guide rails at the sides of the supporting posts. The train was capable of 25 m.p.h., and the cost of the line worked out to about $2,000 per mile.

Nor apparently did Lartigue know of the demonstration of a similar type of line at the 1872 Exposition de Lyon in France. The line, which was the invention of a Monsieur Duchamp, was two-thirds of a mile long, and its single passenger car was drawn by cable.

At any rate, Lartigue must have decided for himself that mules were too slow, for he used an electric

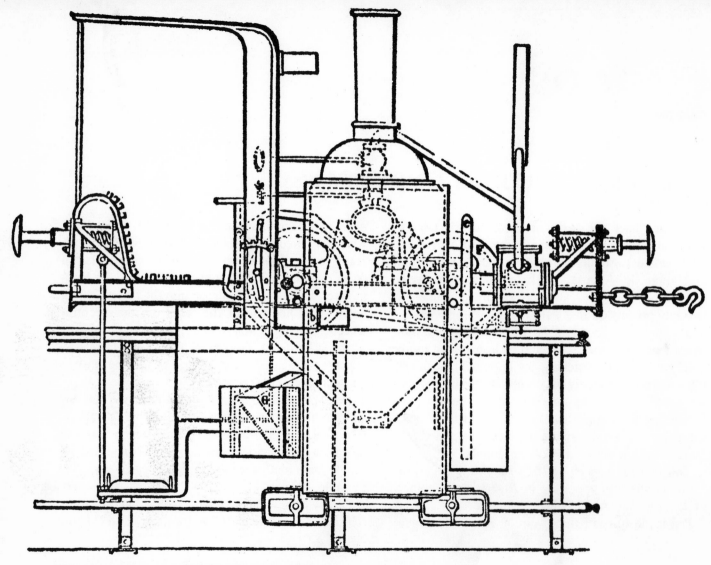

Diagram of the locomotive designed by Mallet for the Lartigue
demonstration at Westminster, London.

Lartigue's demonstration at Westminster in 1886. Note the driver, correctly attired for the occasion.

locomotive on his next monorail. Like General Stone's, Duchamp's, and so many other monorails since, including the present Seattle line, it too was built for an exhibition — the 1884 Agricultural Exhibition in Paris. Five pannier cars fitted with seats, were hauled at a snail's pace by a diminutive 6-h.p. Siemens locomotive, which groaned its way hour after hour through the exhibition grounds with its crowded train of sightseers.

While the public enjoyed it, the railway engineers remained unimpressed, because an electrical supply was not always available in those days. So the indefatigable Lartigue turned to steam, and to England. A passenger line was erected two years later on the site now occupied by Westminster Cathedral in London, the carriages hauled by a magnificent steam locomotive that hissed and whistled and creaked along at six miles an hour. Designed by the brilliant French railroad engineer Mallet and built in Belgium, it had a pair of elegant vertical boilers, two grooved driving wheels, and small horizontal idlers that ran on guide rails along the sides of the trestles. Its driver, a splendid figure in tailcoat and stovepipe hat, rode astride a saddle and stoked the boilers from buckets of coke under his seat.

All the equipment, which included a rack section to show how it could be used for mountain lines, was designed, built and successfully demonstrated in exactly two months — a remarkable achievement, even by present-day standards. And for the first time a monorail aroused serious interest among engineers.

CHAPTER 7

THE LISTOWEL & BALLYBUNION RAILWAY, 1888

Before long, the Lartigue Railway Construction Company — as it was now known — had begun work on a nine-mile track linking Ballybunion, on the west coast of Ireland, with the market town of Listowel. Construction took nine months, and cost only $10,000 a mile including land, rolling stock and equipment. Opened on March 1, 1888, it is the only passenger-carrying monorail ever to have been built for public service in the British Isles.

In addition to the Mallet engine, which was shipped from Westminster and was used for a time, three new locomotives were built by the Hunslet Engine Company in England. Their normal speed was 18 m.p.h., but on occasions, by dint of some furious stoking both by the driver and his fireman, they could be coaxed up to as much as 27 m.p.h.

A visitor who was allowed to ride on the footplate had this to say of his experience: "It is some-what startling to see an apparently fragile trestle arrangement stretching in front of one, in place of the usual solid track. The effect is heightened when the line takes a series of sharp reverse curves, the rail then suggesting a monster serpent of interminable length. The outstanding feature of the monorail locomotive is, however, the motion. It reminds one of riding on a horse attached to a steam roundabout of the undulating type, working at full speed, only more so — very much more so, in fact."

Another slight inconvenience was caused by the peculiar divided construction of the coaches, for when they were full on one side, passengers had to crawl under or over the rail to reach empty compartments on the other side. But this was all part of the fun, and the Irish never complained.

Even though the line was in an argicultural district, it carried as many as 1,400 passengers a day

31

The Listowel & Ballybunion locomotive built by the Hunslet
Engine Company in England.

in the summer and earned itself an enviable reputation for safety. There was only one accident in 36 years of operation, and that was caused by some joker who had unfastened 30 yards of line and placed a timber across the rail. A double-headed train carrying 200 passengers hit the obstacle at full speed, but all that happened was that the derailed locomotives and coaches "dropped gently to the ground without injury or damage."

This comic little railroad continued to operate cheerfully — and at times even to make a profit — until 1924, when rising costs and the growth of the road transport finally forced it out of business.

The Listowel & Ballybunion Railway in Ireland, 1888. This comic little train could hit 27 m.p.h. if both the driver and his fireman stoked the boiler furiously.

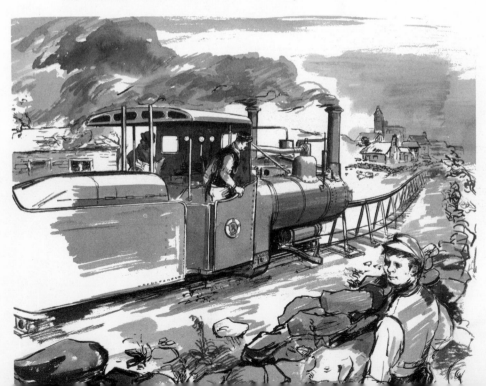

CHAPTER 8

LARTIGUE IN FRANCE AND AMERICA, 1886-1924

Lartigue was assisted in many of his early experiments by his chief engineer, Fritz Bernhard Behr, a brilliant man who was later to become famous in his own right, as we shall see.

In October 1886, Behr gave a lecture before the Society of Engineers, in which he described a particularly ingenious example of the Lartigue monorail, using "regenerative braking" — a then entirely new principle that has since been applied to many mountain and steep-gradient railroads. This particular line, which was 6¾ miles long, was built in the Pyreneees for the Ria copper mines. There were two separate tracks, one for the loaded train carrying the copper ore down the mountainside, and the other returning the empty wagons up to the mine workings. Each was hauled by a Siemens electric locomotive, the motor on the "down" locomotive being used as a dynamo driven by the wheels. This not only had the effect of a powerful brake but it generated sufficient current to haul the empty train back up the mountain.

During the next ten years, Lartigue lines are believed to have been built in Guatemala, Peru, and at St. Petersburg in Russia. There was also a demonstration on Long Island, where a network of electrically worked monorails was planned, radiating from Brooklyn. No more was heard of this, and the records of the others are obscure.

One line, however, did succeed in attracting considerable publicity, if only quite the wrong kind! It was built in France in 1894, linking the townships of Panissières, in the Haute-Loire, and Feurs, 10½ miles away. The rail, passenger cars and the double-boiler locomotive, which was built by the Biatrix works in Saint-Etienne, all closely resembled those at Ballybunion. The trails were a great success, and on

An impression of the steam-hauled Lartigue line at St. Petersburg, Russia. From a contemporary print.

An early photograph of the Lartigue locomotive built for the
Feurs-Panissières line.

The Fordson tractor engine of the Magnesium Monorail, built in California in 1924.

the opening day the train, loaded with officials and local celebrities, puffed merrily out of sight. But scarcely had the cheers died away than there came a distant rumble and a cloud of steam as the track collapsed under the weight, and the inaugural party sank to an undignified halt. An hour later, the angry and disheveled officials arrived back at Panissières station on foot, demanding the demolition of this "engine of death." The subsequent inquiry decided that the line could not operate without grave risks to its passengers, and that was the end of it.

This was virtually the last of the Lartigue lines, although a quarter of a century later, the Sierra Salt Corporation of Los Angeles built a 30-mile length of track on the Lartigue principle to transport magnesium salts from their mine in the Crystal Hills to the Trona railhead. The route lay across the broken, rugged terrain of Salinas Valley, Inyo County, and the trestle type of monorail was chosen for its low cost.

The rail was spiked onto A frames of Douglas fir, and the simple steel-framed wagons, which were split Lartigue-style by their central wheels, were hauled by equally rudimentary locomotives with Fordson tractor gasoline engines. Money was saved wherever possible — even on the couplings, which were salvaged from scrapped Los Angeles trolley-cars — and at first no stabilizing wheels were fitted. The result was that the trains swayed wildly at anything over 15 m.p.h., and short vertical axles had to be added, carrying steel rollers that ran along wooden planks fastened to the A frames.

From now on the "Epsom Salts Line" became a thundering success. The safe maximum speed increased to 35 m.p.h., and the resultant rumbling of rollers on timber at this speed could be heard for miles. But the success was short-lived, for competition by more modern methods of magnesium extraction forced the mine to close two years later, and the line was abandoned.

The "Epsom Salts" train thunders through Saline Valley. Note the driver's sunshade.

CHAPTER 9

FRITZ BERNHARD BEHR, 1897-1904

Behr was an engineer of considerable experience. A pupil of Sir John Fowler, he had worked on the Metropolitan and the Irish Midland and Great Western Railways. During his association with the Lartigue system, he formed his own ideas about adapting it for a high-speed monorail, and with the encouragement of King Leopold II of Belgium he built an experimental line adjoining the Brussels Exhibition of 1897.

The car was a gigantic streamlined affair weighing 55 tons, with long galleries of luxurious seats running down either side in four rows. It was carried on two massive four-wheel bogies, driven by electric motors totaling 600 h.p., and there were double sets of stabilizing wheels that ran on twin rails on either side of the support trestles. Top speed was estimated at 120 m.p.h., and special attention was paid to braking, which was a combination of mechanical and electrical with special louvres that could be extended to act as air brakes at this tremendous speed.

Watched by representatives of the Belgian, Russian and French governments, the monster — after one or two false starts when the newly built power station found itself unable to supply any current — roared off round the little three-mile circuit at over 80 m.p.h. Given a longer track and better power supply, there was little doubt that it could have gone much faster. The government officials were surprised and impressed — but apparently did nothing about it.

Behr returned to England and made plans for a monorail which would *average* 110 m.p.h. between Liverpool and Manchester, using 1,500 h.p. to attain this speed within two minutes of starting. In an interview with the Liverpool *Journal of Commerce,* his promotors claimed that "the block system of the Electric Express will be infinitely superior to anything now in existence. Signals, for one thing, will be done away with — at least, the signals which now wave their arms mysteriously and are invisible in a fog. The Electrical Expresses cannot 'telescope' each other in the rear, or crash into each other like mad bulls head to head, while splintered carriages are piled sky-high, and the blood and the groans of the dead and the dying issue from the mangled mass of wood and iron. The conductor of the Electrical Express has a dial before him, the sensitive pointers on which tell him exactly how far the train before him is in front, and how far the train behind him is in the rear, fog or no fog; the apparatus locates an obstruction on the line as accurately as the Post Office officials find out a break in the telegraph wires; consequently the Electric Express is safety itself. As for curves, they present no difficulty. The express can wriggle round them with the greatest ease."

A bill to authorize the line came before Parliament in 1900. Fiercely opposed by the existing railways, the proposals were rejected because, it was said, "no safe way of applying brake power to these very high speed trains had yet been demonstrated."

Behr persevered, and after further lengthy debates in both houses of Parliament, an amended scheme was authorized a year later as the Manchester-Liverpool Electric Express Railway. But it was later turned down by the Board of Trade, which still had its doubts about the braking system. While this was going on, Behr put forward a scheme for a 150-m.p.h. monorail from London to Brighton, only to have it squashed on parliamentary procedure by the existing railway, who promptly sought authority to electrify its own line. A private company was then formed to build a seven-mile length of track on which the monorail could prove itself, but the project gradually ran short of capital. It was finally abandoned in 1906, and Behr disappeared from the public eye.

Demonstration of the 55-ton Behr monorail at the Brussels Exhibition in 1897. It achieved over 80 m.p.h. round the three-mile circuit.

CHAPTER 10

THE WUPPERTAL "SWINGING RAILWAY," 1901

Wuppertal is a large industrial center in West Germany, sprawling eleven miles along the valley of the River Wupper from which it took its name. Often referred to as "Busy Lizzie" because it employs a higher percentage of women than any other city in the Federal Republic, Wuppertal is widely known for its chemicals, textiles and metals. But it is the *Schwebebahn,* or Swinging Railway, that has made it famous all over the world.

Around the turn of the last century Eugen Langen, a resourceful civil engineer from Cologne, conceived the idea of a transportation system which would link Barmen, Elberfeld and Vohwinkel — separate towns in those days, but now districts of Wuppertal — much more cheaply than could a conventional railway. Langen may have seen reports of the Enos railway in the United States; or perhaps he reinvented the system for himself. At any rate,

instead of driving the tracks through the towns, demolishing buildings and paying large sums for the right-of-way across people's property, Langen planned to suspend his rail cars from twin overhead lines which would, for most of the route, follow the narrow, winding bed of the river.

Alas, Langen did not live to see his railway. He died in 1895, soon after selling his rights to a Nuremberg firm, Continentale Gessellschaft für Elecktrische Unternehmungen, who had agreed to construct a short experimental length of track.

This they did, and the city fathers were so impressed by this new method of travel that they quickly voted the funds for a full-length line. The cost incidentally, worked out at less than half that of a conventional elevated railway, and only a quarter as much as an underground system. But while the early tests were still being run, it was discovered

Photo: John R. Day

The famous German monorail, built in 1901 and still in every-day service.

that the motion of the cars could be made smoother and the speed around the curves doubled by using one rail instead of two. So a monorail it became.

The first 2¾-mile section of the new railway was officially opened to the public on March 1, 1901, and by 1903 it had been extended to its full length of about 9 miles. Today, more than sixty years and two World Wars later, it is still operating profitably and has now carried more than one thousand *million* passengers in its "flying coal boxes," as a visitor once called the reddish-brown cars.

Sloping lattice girders carry the two single rails — the trains run in both directions, passing one another closely — some 40 feet above the surface of the water, sweeping in here and there to run down the center of a street before rejoining the river. There are 18 elevated stations along the route, sandwiched between the offices, department stores, factories and blocks of flats.

Each 12-ton car, two to a train, is suspended below a pair of twin-wheel tandem bogies, each bogie being driven by an electric motor of 30 h.p. — increased to 60 h.p. in the cars that have been built more recently. Maximum permitted speed is 30 m.p.h. This is seldom achieved in everyday service, however, the normal average being nearer to 15 m.p.h. Signaling is entirely automatic, operated by

Winding its way along the Wupper River and through the city like an iron centipede.

47

Wuppertal's swinging railway, iron backbone of an industrial city.

the trains themselves on a station-to-station block system. There is also a telephone on each train, so that the station behind or ahead can be contacted in an emergency. Another interesting feature is the braking system which works from compressed air stored in steel tubes under the car, the supply being recharged when the train reaches the terminal station at either end of the line.

The earlier cars had 25 seats and standing room for 40, but in the new ones, purchased in 1951 to meet the increasing traffic, the passenger capacity was stepped up to 80. With the trains running every two minutes during peak periods, the total load often exceeds 4,000 passengers per hour in each direction.

Yet from the day it was built, this picturesque and now antiquated railway has never had an accident due to derailment or structural failure; and rain, snow and fog have never upset its clockwork regularity. The line itself was severely damaged by bombing during World War II, being kept going in sections until it was put completely out of action during the heavy raids of 1943. By Easter 1946, however, it had been repaired and the iron centipedes were once more crawling slowly and surely through the throbbing heart of Wuppertal. Indeed, the only real incident that anyone can remember was when an energetic baby elephant, traveling to a circus site, bolted through the doors and landed unceremoniously in the river.

CHAPTER 11

BRENNAN GYROSCOPIC MONORAIL, 1909

To run a train on a single rail laid on the ground without the expense and complication of any overhead structure — this was the dream of Louis Brennan, an Irishman who first won fame in 1882 as the inventor of a torpedo controlled by wires from the shore.

He began experimenting with monorails soon afterward, patenting his invention of a gyroscopically balanced car in 1903 and exhibiting a working model of it four years later to the Royal Society in London. While the full-size car was still being developed, the German pioneer August Scherl was building a gyro-monorail of his own design. Hearing that there was to be a public exhibition of it in the Berlin Zoo on November 10, 1909, Brennan hurriedly arranged a demonstration to the press of his own car on the same day, at Gillingham, Kent.

It was built primarily as a military vehicle, on account of the speed with which the single track could be laid, and it was powered by gasoline engines: electricity supplies could not be relied on in military operations and a cloud of steam might reveal the car's position to the enemy. An 80-h.p. engine drove an electric generator feeding current to motors on each of the two-wheel bogies, and a separate 20-h.p. engine and generator supplied the gyroscope motor. The gyroscope contained a pair of 42-inch-diameter wheels, spinning in opposite directions at 3,000 revolutions per minute inside a vacuum casing.

The gyroscopic force from these wheels, which between them weighed 1½ tons, was sufficient not only to keep the empty car upright on its single rail, claimed Brennan, but to resist the weight of 40 passengers all standing on one side of the vehicle. The press was invited to do this while the car was travel-

51

Below: The inventor, Louis Brennan, and his monorail car.

Photos: Railway Gazette

Left and above: The first demonstration at Gillingham, England, on November 10, 1909, of Brennan's monorail. High-speed gyroscopes kept it balanced, even when all the passengers moved to one side.

ing round the track. Instead of that side sinking as the weight came on, it rose slightly, the gyroscope over-compensating for a second or two before-reaching equilibrium.

It looked uncanny, especially when the car automatically banked inwards as it took the curves — like a cyclist. The inertia stored in the flywheels was sufficient to keep the car upright for quite a long time after the current had been switched off. It would then slowly lean over and come to rest against its props.

Nevertheless, despite a series of successful demonstrations to scientists, engineers and military officers, the awful fear of the gyroscope somehow stopping prevented Brennan's car from ever being used for public transportation.

Scherl's, which was widely exhibited in the States, was given the same verdict, and it was left to Peter Schilovsky, a Russian nobleman, to carry the torch for gyro-monorails. He almost succeeded, when in 1921 the Russian government decided on a 20-mile Schilovsky line from Petrograd to Tsarskoye Selo. But after seven miles had been built, the project was abandoned for lack of finance. With modern monorails having reached such an advanced state of perfection, it seems unlikely that we shall see a return to the railroad gyroscope.

CITY ISLAND RAILROAD, 1910

The fastest monorail ever to operate commercially was built in 1910, by August Belmont, to carry passengers between Long Island City and the New Haven Railroad station 1½ miles away. It covered the distance in exactly 1½ minutes, an average of 60 m.p.h., and did this regularly every day — while it lasted.

Designed by H. H. Tunis, the Flying Lady, as the car was called, looked like a single-deck tramcar, with pointed ends and rows of glass windows along the sides. Under it were four double-flanged wheels, running on a single rail and driven by electric motors on the axles. Overhead stabilizing rails and horizontal guide wheels on the roof prevented the car from toppling over, and also supplied the current for the motors.

An overhead stabilized monorail had already been seen on Long Island back in 1892. This was the famous Boynton Bicycle Railroad, a steam-driven flyer that also clocked a regular 60 m.p.h. The locomotive was two stories high, with an engineer upstairs and a fireman below, and had a single 8-foot-diameter driving wheel. It operated successfully for two years.

The Flying Lady, however, ran for only three months before it met with a serious accident. This was caused by faulty construction of the rail framework, and by the very feature that gave the car its high speed: the overhead rails that banked the car on curves so that they could be taken without slowing down. One day the motorman, for some reason, eased down to 45 m.p.h. on a curve that should have been taken at 55. Feeling the lack of stability, he slowed down even more, the guide wheels slipped out of the flimsy top rails and the car, crowded with 100 passengers, crashed over onto its side. There were many injuries, and the subsequent legal expenses put the line out of-business.

But the idea of "wheels top and bottom" had already attracted attention in England, where E. W. C. Kearney had proposed a car on this principle for subway railways, both upper and lower rails being mounted direct on the tunnel lining. Unlike the Tunis design, Kearney's had vertical stabilizing wheels pressed upwards from the roof onto the top rail by compressed air. This compensated for any irregularities in the spacing between the rails, so that the car could not slip out from between them.

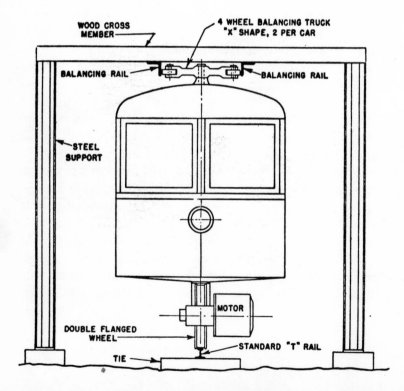

Front view of the Flying Lady monorail car designed by H. H. Tunis, showing the overhead balancing rails.

An impression of the Flying Lady banking like an airplane
on a high-speed curve.

The 1909 Kearney monorail car, seen here on temporary transportation trolleys at the Brush Electrical Engineering Co. factory at Loughborough, England.

A 45-passenger car, electrically driven by motors on each of its four in-line wheels, was built in 1909 by the Brush Company of Loughborough, England; but it was destroyed by fire before it could be demonstrated.

Like Behr before him, the inventor made numerous proposals over the years for the use of his electric subway express in Britain and elsewhere, even visiting Moscow when its underground railway was first projected in an unsuccessful attempt to interest the Russian authorities in his system. For three decades, a succession of committees, delegations and public bodies urged the adoption of the Kearney subway. Twice the decision was taken to go ahead and twice — in 1914 and 1939 — a World War prevented work from starting. Yet today in 1963, after half a century of disappointment, E. W. C. Kearney is still an enthusiastic and active advocator of the monorail.

Photo: Glasgow Herald

The Bennie Railplane on the test track near Glasgow, Scotland, in 1929.

CHAPTER 13

THE BENNIE RAILPLANE, 1929

The period of stagnation in railroad engineering between the wars produced only one new monorail, but this at least offered exciting prospects. It provided air-travel speeds — or so it was claimed — with railroad safety and reliability in all weathers. And indeed it looked a cross between the two forms of transportation.

The invention of George Bennie, a Scottish engineer, the Railplane had a torpedo-shaped car, driven by an airplane propeller at each end, and suspended from two two-wheeled bogies running on an elevated rail. Below it was a second girder, gripped on either side by horizontal guide wheels under the car. Power for each propeller came from a 60-h.p. electric motor, specially designed so that it could deliver 240 h.p. in a short burst for accelerating to the cruising speed of over 100 m.p.h. There

was automatic signaling, and automatic braking if the signals were ignored.

It all sounded fine, and worked as well as could be expected on the short test track, built in 1929 over a disused railroad near Glasgow, Scotland. There were brave plans for a high-speed link between London and Paris, using a Railplane as far as Folkstone, a seaplane for the English Channel crossing to Boulogne, and another Railplane on to Paris. There were schemes to carry airline passengers from the heart of London to its airports at Croydon and Heston, and to serve the commuter traffic in Glasgow, Blackpool and other cities. But the grave economic difficulties faced by Britain in the early 1930's doomed Bennie's invention from the start. None of his lines was ever built, and the car and test track were finally dismantled a few years ago.

CHAPTER 14

ALWEG, MONORAIL, COLOGNE-FUHLINGEN, 1952

The choked highways and traffic jams that followed the upsurge in automobile production after World War II led to a renewed interest in monorails as a means of relieving the congestion. From 1950 onward, a considerable number of projects were announced, notably by U.S. airplane manufacturers seeking new outlets for their fast-emptying factories.

But the first postwar monorail to get past the blueprint stage was the Alweg system, the creation of Swedish industrialist Dr. Axel Wenner-Gren. It was erected at Fühlingen in West Germany, next door to the ancient Rhine port of Cologne, and it made its debut in October 1952.

Because Dr. Wenner-Gren saw the monorail as an integral unit of modern transportation — a supplement rather than a replacement — he studied the problems inherent in building a monorail around existing facilities: in short, how to avoid a massive dislocation of the normal traffic flow.

Cologne, its medieval city center a maze of narrow streets, was a most appropriate place in which to tackle such difficulties. The result was the formulation of unique speed-up construction techniques that have since been patented and incorporated in the Alweg system, by which the 1¼-mile oval beamway at Cologne-Fühlingen was completed in less than twelve months.

The test train, built to a scale of two-fifths full size, was skinned in gleaming aluminum — in strong contrast to the utility look of earlier systems. And the beamway adopted the clean lines of modern architecture, with continuous lengths of reinforced concrete spanning T-shaped pylons.

Technically, as well as aesthetically, Dr. Wenner-Gren aimed for simplicity. And the rightness of his

The first full-size Alweg car on the test track built at Cologne-Fühlingen, West Germany.

Right: Underside of the Alweg car, showing the main supporting wheels, stabilizing wheels, and the steel safety wheels which come into operation in the event of a tire blowout.

Left: The side pockets of the Alweg car can be raised for convenient access to the power equipment.

original design has since been proved, not only on the test track but by the other Alweg monorails that have since entered service.

The Alweg train comprises two or three flexible-jointed or articulated cars, each mounted on two four-wheel bogies driven by a pair of 100- to 150-h.p. electric motors, with four horizontal stabilizing wheels gripping the beamway below each bogie. For smooth and silent running, all the wheels are fitted with pneumatic rubber tires which also permit very high rates of acceleration and braking. Current for the motors is picked up from contact rails along the beam by collector shoes in the side pockets of the car. There, in the side pockets, all the motors, brakes, and automatic control equipment are located for ease of access.

Between 1952 and 1957, four more scaled-down test trains were built and tested on the Fühlingen track, at times reaching speeds of nearly 100 m.p.h. The test program completed, they were superseded, in July 1957, by the first full-size Alweg car which is still in use today for demonstration purposes.

CHAPTER 15

SKYWAY MONORAILS, 1956

The first U.S. monorail for nearly thirty years was seen at Houston, Texas, in 1956. Built in Arrowhead Park by Monorail, Inc., at a cost of $100,000, it was a 300-yard test line for a new system named the Skyway. The track was in the form of a 30-inch tube, flattened on top to present a running surface, and supported on tubular steel pillars shaped like an inverted J. The air-conditioned 60-seat car, built of fiber glass and weighing 12 tons, was suspended from two four-wheel rubber-tired bogies, which ran along the flat top of the rail, with horizontal guide wheels engaging a vertical flange welded along the rail center. Each bogie was powered by a 310-h.p. Packard automobile engine, and above one of the bogies sat the driver in an elevated cab.

After eight months of testing, the track was dismantled and rebuilt the same year, with a number of improvements, for the Texas State Fair at Dallas. Extended to 500 yards in length, it regularly reached 60 m.p.h. with a full load of sightseeing passengers. Its promoters claimed 100-m.p.h. capability with a longer line, and plans were made for Skyway installations in Florida, but they were never built.

Photo: John R. Day
Skyway demonstration line at Houston, Texas, 1956. The car was driven by two Packard automobile engines and was built of fiber glass.

SAFEGE "SUSPENDED METRO," 1958

The chief rival to the Alweg and other straddle types of monorail is a suspended system, under development by SAFEGE Transport, a consortium of eighteen French firms, including a number of major banks, electrical and civil engineers, and the famous Renault and Michelin companies.

In 1947 the eminent French bridge builder Louis Chadenson became interested in the Bennie experimental line which still existed at that time at Glasgow, Scotland. Later he was impressed by the success of the Paris Metro's Route 11, whose trains had been adapted to run on rubber tires, and he decided to combine the two principles. One of the difficulties, however, was that rubber loses much of its grip in wet weather. And whereas the Paris Metro is underground, Chadenson's railway was to be built in the open air.

Examining ways and means of keeping the track

dry he realized that, if the car could be suspended under the bogies, it would be possible to put a roof over the track. This gave him the idea of running the bogies not on a rail but *inside* a continuous box girder, with a narrow slit along its underside for the supports linking the bogies to the car.

With French government backing, a big research program got under way in 1952; six years later a mile of experimental track began operating at Châteauneuf, some 90 miles south of Paris.

The original track was built of steel, but later sections are in prestressed concrete, which is much cheaper and quicker to erect. The box rail is supported every 100 feet or so by slender, concrete-filled steel pylons. These occupy very little space on the ground, so that the SAFEGE system can be built above a conventional railway, or along the center of any reasonably wide street. Each 60-seat car is

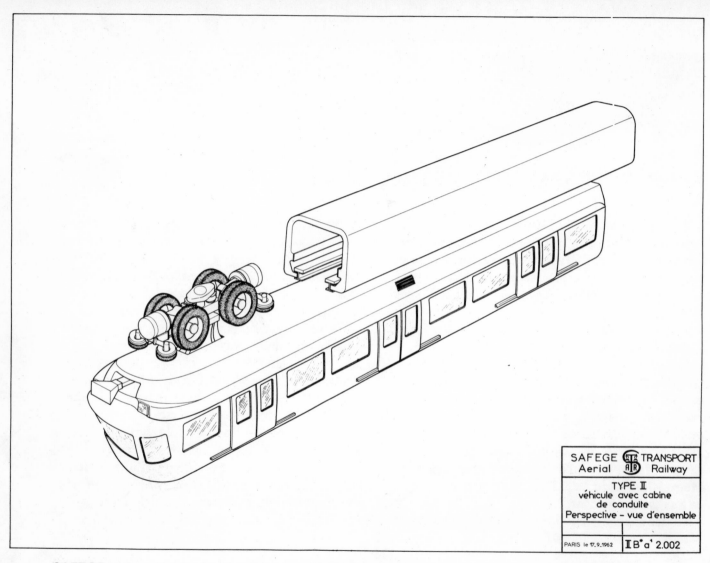

SAFEGE Ⓢ TRANSPORT
Aerial Ⓐ Railway

TYPE II
véhicule avec cabine
de conduite
Perspective – vue d'ensemble

PARIS le 17.9.1962 | II B*a⁴ 2.002

SAFEGE monorail car, showing the box girder which forms
the track, and one of the two electrically powered bogies.

A 60-seater SAFEGE car under test on the experimental track at Châteauneuf, near Paris.

A close-up of the SAFEGE bogie, showing the nitrogen-inflated rubber tires, electric driving motors at either end, and the horizontal stabilizing wheels.

suspended from two four-wheel bogies, similar in design to those used in the Paris Metro, with four small horizontal guide wheels bearing on the sides of the box rail to give lateral stability.

All the wheels are fitted with pneumatic tires, which have a life of about 125,000 miles. In the rare event of a tire blowout, the weight is taken on steel safety rims. The tires themselves are inflated with nitrogen to reduce the risk of fire if they should become overheated and because less pressure is lost by diffusion, or seepage through the rubber, than would occur with compressed air. In addition to being smooth and silent running, the tenacious grip of the tires allows the train to climb gradients as steep as one-in-six, which would be quite impossible with steel-wheeled bogies, and to accelerate very rapidly — from a standstill to 60 m.p.h. in five seconds, for example. Braking is equally powerful: a fully laden train can be crash stopped in a little over 100 yards from 60 m.p.h. But this is done only in an emergency, because the passengers are liable to slide off their seats and finish up on the floor. Indeed, passenger comfort, rather than power and wheel adhesion, is the limiting factor in acceleration and deceleration.

Each of the two bogies is driven by a pair of 100-h.p. electric motors, giving a normal cruising

72

speed of 70 m.p.h. Current at 750 volts D.C. is picked up by miniature pantographs from live conductors inside the box rail, which also houses the automatic signaling cables. With virtually all the working parts protected in this way from the weather, the experimental line has been operated regularly through fog, snow and ice — conditions which usually make roads and conventional railways hazardous at best.

The tests have been witnessed by officials and engineers from many countries during visits to the installation at Châteauneuf. Agreements or options have already been signed with the major industrial groups in Britain, Japan and Italy to build SAFEGE systems there, and among other interested countries, the Soviet Union is known to be considering a version of it, built under French supervision, to link Moscow with Sheremetieva international airport.

Photo: John R. Day

Alweg trains cross one another during their one-mile run through Disneyland, California.

CHAPTER 17

ALWEG, DISNEYLAND, 1959

The first Alweg monorail for fare-paying passengers was built in Disneyland in Anaheim, California. The line, with two three-car trains, was opened on June 14, 1959 — just six months after initial planning sessions, and well-timed for the summer rush of visitors.

Like everything else in Disneyland, the monorail was tailored to a scale five-eighths normal size. Appropriately, it was sited in Tomorrowland. The mile-long beamway — a split-level figure eight — threads through landscaped gardens and rises to 35 feet in some places. The open-windowed trains, each with room for 100 passengers, quickly became Sightseers' Specials. Traveling at a leisurely 25 m.p.h., they provide a grandstand view of Disneyland, telescoped into a brilliant montage of familiar Disney characters.

After two profitable years of operation — four million passengers in the first year — it was decided to build another two miles of track in order to provide a monorail link between the Disneyland Hotel and the auto parking area. To run this shuttle service, a third train — with four cars this time — was added to the Disneyland fleet. At about the same time, the two original trains were rebuilt to incorporate a fourth car.

The Disneyland monorail is still in service. In appearance, it is noticeably different from its German parent: the pylons are single concrete columns tapering upward from a broad base, and the trains themselves are more streamlined, looking rather like sleek modern airliners minus wings. If its novelty appeal has diminished a little, it is still a star turn, averaging about 175,000 passengers a week.

Photo: La Vie du Rail
Japan's first monorail, built in 1957 as a test line in the Ueno
Park Zoological Gardens, Tokyo.

CHAPTER 18

TOKYO MONORAILS, 1957-1961

Japan, engaged in an all-out effort to improve its transportation system, is spending hundreds of millions every year on new railroad and highway projects, but the nation's economy is still seriously hampered by inadequate communications. This is especially true in Tokyo, now the most populous city in the world. With Japan's population of 93 million squeezed into a country little bigger than the State of California, the Japanese authorities began experimenting with monorails to ease suburban traffic loads in Tokyo.

The first was built in 1957 as a test line by the Tokyo metropolitan government, in the Ueno Park Zoological Gardens. Four hundred yards long, it look like a modernized version of the Wuppertal Swinging Railway, with a two-car train suspended from electric bogies running on an elevated steel-and-concrete track. Each six-ton coach, seating 31 passengers, is built largely of aluminum alloy and plastics and is powered by two 40-h.p. motors driving on rubber tires, with guide wheels contacting the sides of the box girder forming the track. Costs were kept to a minimum by using stock steel and standard mechanisms, and operating speed is only 8½ m.p.h.

In its first year of service it carried over a million passengers, but it developed several bugs. Although these were rectified and the line is still operating, it is significant that subsequent Japanese installations have all been of the supported type, as instanced by the Dreamland miniature line built in 1961 by Tokyo Shibaura Electric in the grounds of Nara amusement park, and other lines.

Photo: Tokyo Shibaura Electric Co.

Toshiba monorail in the Dreamland amusement park, Nara,
1961.

CHAPTER 19

ALWEG, TURIN, 1961

Lessons learned from the building of the miniature monorail in Disneyland and during its first few months of intensive operation were soon put to good use in another country. During the winter of 1960-1961, work was started on a full-scale Alweg line, of normal suburban train size, at Turin in northern Italy.

This important industrial center, home of the world-famous Fiat automobile company, had been chosen as the host city for the Italia 61 Exhibition to mark Italy's national centenary. As well as providing a rapid link between the main entrance and the exhibition's center, the monorail was expected to be a crowd-pulling attraction, and engineers worked against the clock to complete the job in time.

The line was officially opened on May 6, 1961, just seven months after the first planning discussions. The single track, three-quarters of a mile long, was built north-south along the busy Corso Polonia auto-strada, with a terminal station at each end. The streamlined three-car train, driven by three 150-horsepower electric motors (one in each car) ran 18 feet above road-level, and could reach a top speed of 50 m.p.h. in less than 20 seconds from a standstill. This rapid acceleration was due to the grip of the rubber-tired wheels.

As anticipated, the Turin monorail was a great success, and over one and a half million passengers had traveled on the line when the exhibition closed in October 1961. The cars were usually packed to capacity, with tourists strap-hanging like rush-hour commuters, as they craned to see the panoramic view of the city and its ancient and beautiful buildings. Plans to operate the monorail on a permanent basis, and eventually to extend it to Moncalieri in the southern suburbs and downtown Turin, have been shelved for the time being.

Left: Three-car Alweg train at Turin, Italy. The track was built for the 1961 Exhibition and carried 1$^1/_2$ million passengers in six months.

Right: The single Alweg track at Turin, Italy, runs above the autostrada and through the exhibition grounds.

Right: Interior of an Alweg car at Turin.

Photo: Alweg
Left: Straphanging sightseers disembark from the Turin monorail.

Close-up of the Alweg-Hitachi car, showing the side pockets housing the electrical equipment.

CHAPTER 20

ALWEG, INUYAMA, 1962

Following the interest aroused in Japan by the earlier monorails, a one-mile line was built on the Alweg principle by Hitachi, linking the central railway station at Inuyama with the outskirts of the city. The single-line track includes some steep gradients — up to 9.7 percent — and there are three stations.

Like the Disneyland monorail, the Inuyama track was completed in a bare six months. It was opened on March 21, 1962, and is a good illustration of the adaptability of the Alweg system. Because Inuyama lies very close to a popular resort visited by many hundreds of tourists every year, the Japanese authorities sensibly decided to have two trains, both three-car units, which could be flexibly coupled, when needed, to cope with height-of-the-season crowds.

The Alweg-Hitachi line at Inuyama, Japan, showing a six-car
unit in operation.

CHAPTER 21

ALWEG, SEATTLE, 1962

The most important date in Alweg history was probably April 21, 1962, the opening day of the Century 21 World's Fair in Seattle, It was important because it began the first practical demonstration of the Alweg monorail in its intended role: a transport system to relieve the crippling traffic congestion in built-up areas.

The Seattle city authorities knew that thousands of visitors would be coming to see the Fair. They also knew that with any sizable influx of automobiles and motor coaches, road traffic in the city's center would soon become a solid, unmoving mass. And so they decided to build a monorail — the Alweg, which they had already seen in operation at Disneyland.

Ten months later it was completed, a 1.2-mile double-track beamway, carried on 25-foot-high py-lons, from downtown Pine Street to the Fair. Nearly 1,000 tons of steel and 15,000 tons of concrete were used in its construction. The two trains were identified by a band of color along the roofline and waist, and became known as the Red train and the Blue train. Each was a four-car unit with room for 450 passengers, designed for a maximum speed of 70 m.p.h., although this was usually kept to 50-60 m.p.h. for the benefit of the nervous.

In other respects everything was designed for top-speed service. A train left the city terminal for the exhibition site every five minutes. Turn-around time was practically nil, because not only could the trains be driven from either end, but the terminals were designed for simultaneous loading and unloading — passengers were conveyed by moving rubber belts to the departure platform, where they were able to board

The four-car Alweg monorail winds its way through the center of Seattle.

Alweg monorail travelers ride high above the Seattle traffic on Fifth Avenue.

the train as soon as it came in, while the newly arrived passengers disembarked onto a second platform on the other side of the beamway.

About 50 percent of all visitors went to the Fair by monorail — one million a month from April to October when the Fair closed. The 95-second journey would have taken about 20 minutes by automobile in peak-hour traffic, besides which, there was no better way of touring Seattle. The monorail, which can handle rush-hour traffic equivalent to 16 lanes of automobile freeway, is now a permanent part of Seattle's transport services.

Downtown terminal of the Alweg Seattle monorail.

Modern monorails are good-lookers. This picture shows how the Alweg installation blends with Seattle's architecture.

CHAPTER 22

NIHON-LOCKHEED MONORAIL, 1962-1963

The latest design to appear in the monorail field was conceived by the Lockheed Aircraft Corporation of California and built toward the end of 1962 by Kawasaki Aircraft in Japan. These two organizations, together with six other prominent Japanese concerns, jointly established the Nihon-Lockheed Monorail Company in May 1961 to develop and market the new system, which is currently being demonstrated to potential customers on a half-mile test track in the grounds of Kawasaki Aircraft's plant at Gifu.

Not unlike the Alweg unit in general appearance, the Nihon-Lockheed monorail is a beam-straddler, riding on top of a single steel rail mounted on a prestressed concrete track beam. Each car, weighing 21 tons fully loaded, accommodates 48 seated and 72 standing passengers in a soundproofed cabin.

Self-leveling air springs support the car on two trucks, each having two main wheels, four horizontal guide wheels gripping the sides of the rail, and two more stabilizing wheels running lower down along the sides of the track beam. An interesting feature of all the wheels is that instead of using pneumatic tires, they are of integral steel-and-rubber construction, like a sandwich. There are also, in the interests of safety, three independent braking systems: one electrical, using the motors; air brakes on the wheels; and caliper pads to grip the rail itself. Four 100-h.p. electric motors per car give a service speed of 75 m.p.h.

Latest news of the Nihon-Lockheed monorail is that it has been chosen to link Tokyo airport with the city center, and construction work on the eight-mile line began in May 1963.

Testing a two-car Nihon-Lockheed monorail at Gifu, Japan. Note the stabilizing wheels gripping the bottom of the beamway.

Nihon-Lockheed test track under construction in the grounds of Kawasaki Aircraft showing the steel rail on top of the beamway.

Driving position in the Nihon-Lockheed car. The upper stabilizing wheels can be seen under the cab, gripping the sides of the rail.

Glimpse of the future: a working model of the Ford Levacar,
a 200-passenger vehicle driven at 500 m.p.h. by gas turbines.

CHAPTER 23

FORD LEVACAR

Future trends are clearly indicated in the working model, by the Ford Motor Company, of a 200-passenger vehicle that may some day shuttle between major city centers at speeds of up to 500 m.p.h.

The great speed is possible because the vehicles will have practically no friction to overcome. Instead of using wheels, they will slide on a thin film of air, pumped by turbo-compressors to pads that skid along the rail. Gas turbine-driven shrouded propellers will drive the Levacar along, under automatic remote control. It makes an interesting comparison with George Bennie's 1929 Railplane, pictured on page 60.

INDEX

THE AUTHOR

Derek Harvey, an English citizen, is presently the Executive Director, Public Relations, Hawker Siddeley Industries Ltd., as well as technical correspondent for various Continental magazines, the B.B.C. and Britain's Central Office of Information. In the past ten years, he has contributed over four hundred articles and radio scripts on engineering and aviation subjects. Mr. Harvey has traveled in or on everything imaginable, from hydrofoil to camel. It was his ride on a German monorail that intrigued him into writing the book.